LOOKING FOR GROUP

VOLUME 1

Blind Ferret Entertainment presents:

LOOKING FOR GROUP

Volume 1

Ryan Sohmer
Writer

Lar deSouza
Artist

Randy Waxman
President & CEO

Nick Di Feo
Sales Manager

Ryan Sohmer
Vice President, Creative Director

Ryan McCahan
Technical Director

Marc Aflalo
Media Director & Public Relations Manager

Ghislain Leduc
Community Manager

Lar deSouza
Art Director

www.lfgcomic.com

ISBN 978-0-9736946-4-2

I don't play MMORPGs.

Not only do I find that acronym far too unweildy to pronounce, but I feel that a game like World of Warcraft would prove very addictive and draw me away from more important pursuits--like reading webcomics.

So it was that I put off reading Looking For Group. Now, I was well aware that Sohmer was an extremely talented (not to mention gregarious) writer. I also knew that Lar deSouza was probably one of the very best (if not the best) cartoonists working in webcomics at the time. But I figured that since I didn't play WoW, I wouldn't understand **Looking For Group.**

I was wrong; I made a mistake. It happens on rare occasion. (Like that time I misspelled unwieldy. Man, was that embarrassing.)

You don't have to read Beowulf to love Tolkien. You don't have to have lived in Giverny to appreciate Monet's paintings. And you don't have to have played WoW to have a lot of fun reading **Looking for Group**. Once I came around, I found myself enjoying the comic immensely. So much so, in fact, that I was honored when Sohmer emailed me and asked if I'd write this introduction.

If You Haven't Read Looking For Group in its Online form. . .

You're in for a treat.

This comic represents part of what I see as a certain coming of age movement in the webcomics genre. Like fantasy novels in the 1970s, webcomics in the 2000s are finding their place as a professional, respectable entertainment medium which is drawing serious talent. **Looking For Group** is one of the stories at the forefront of this professionalization of webcomics, and includes some of the finest art, storytelling, and humor you're likely to find anywhere on the web.

And it also involves copious face-melting!

Consider that both a promise and a warning. This story can get a tad violent. The student of literature, however, will look at this piece and see it as a complex treatment of good, evil, and conscience. Cale's exaggerated sense of honor in the face of Richard's diabolical foil sets the backdrop for an exploration of what it means to be innocent, then lose that innocence. The text may challenge you, dear reader, to examine your own morals and ask yourself to what lengths you might be willing to go in order to see justice done.

That's what the student of literature might say. Fortunately, we all know that students of literature should have their faces melted for thinking about things way too much. This comic is about having fun, first and foremost. And let me promise you, it does that very, very well. In this text you will find parodies of famous fantasy stories, character driven humor, mystical forks, imps who talk way too fast, and sarcasm galore.

Plus, did I mention the face-melting?

(Note: For those who are still disturbed by the prospect of sadistic undead warlock protagonists eating babies on a regular basis, I offer the following list for your consideration:

A)   The heroes have a priestess on their team, and you can pretend she's in the background resurrecting the aforementioned snacked-upon babies.

B)   Death in this world isn't really all that bad. You can still talk even after you've been turned into a pile of ash, and if you're lucky, you might end up turning into a sadistic undead warlock protagonist yourself.

C)   Those babies were totally asking for it.)

If You Have Read Looking For Group Online. . . .

You're in for a treat too.

In my opinion, one of the defining features of the webcomic genre is its abil-
ity to evolve and reinvent itself even as the story progresses. The slow, yet steady, progress of such comics is both one of their greatest liabilities and one of their greatest advantages. The creators are usually forced to publish early pages of a story even as they're working on the later pages.

This forces the creators to be, well, creative. When I write a novel, I have the option to revise early chapters as often as I want to make them consistent with what I end up doing with ending. Webtoonists usually don't have this luxury. Once a strip is published, it becomes cannon--and it must be incorporated into the text of the narrative from then on. I suspect that even practiced professionals like Sohmer and Lar evolve their stories and characters as the comic progresses.

What does this mean for you, though?

It means that reading a webcomic in book form is going to give you a very different experience you'll get from following that same comic on-line. With this volume, you can read months worth of comics in minutes. You experience character and plot arcs in sweeping, epic spans. You can watch Cale's growth, learning, and story as if in fast forward, like a time-lapse camera focused on a sprouting tree.

In short, you have the beautiful opportunity to read **Looking For Group** for the first time. . .again.

So what are you doing reading this introduction? Get on with it!

Brandon Sanderson
January, 2008
Best-selling fantasy novelist,
author of ELANTRIS and
the MISTBORN trilogy.

Immaculate Conception

'd be lying if I said this introduction was easy to write, that the words simply fell onto the page in a literary symphony unparalleled in scope and style since the days of William Shakespeare.

To tell you the truth, I'm not clear as to why I'm struggling so much with this. My intention was to provide somewhat of a back-story on the origins of Looking For Group, and perhaps set the tone for the tale that awaits you in just a few more pages.

As is par for the course, however, what I intended and what resulted are two uniquely disparate things.

Such was the case of the birth of the universe containing Cale, Richard, Benny and Krunch.

Ironically enough, we were originally approached by a video game accessory company who was looking to add a comic strip to their website in order to build brand awareness and other fun terms only applicable to MBA students. The concept was simple enough; to create a monthly feature relating to Massively Multiplayer Online Games (MMO, for the uninitiated amongst you).

At the time, I was heavily into World of Warcraft and Everquest 2, thus the opportunity was more than appealing to me. But, as making decisions alone in the past has led to problems and violent chemical explosions, I hastily picked up the phone and dialed Lar.

When I inquired as to whether he thought he was capable of handling a comic series set in a fantasy environment and interested in doing so, his response was filled with laughter tinged with artistic pride that he pulls off so well.

Once the giggling and indignation ended, he empathetically agreed to work on the new fantasy series and we immediately got to work.

Leaving Lar to do some concept art and character designs, I set myself to the task of writing the first page. It was a daunting task, knowing that first page was responsible for setting the balance for everything that was yet to come. Following a 16-hour marathon writing session, I took a step back from the computer to re-read what I thought was the most inspiring, powerful and poignant opening paragraph conceived in the fantasy genre over the last 20 years:

The Wheel of Time turns, and Ages come and pass, leaving memories that become legend. Legend fades to myth, and even myth is long forgotten when the Age that gave it birth comes again. In one Age, called the Third Age by some, an Age yet to come, an Age long past, a wind rose.... The wind was not the beginning. There are neither beginnings nor endings to the turning of the Wheel of time.

But it was a beginning. *

At the time, I was almost 94% certain that I had come up with that solely on my own.

The next morning, after writing a letter of apology to Robert Jordan and anyone who had ever read The Wheel of Time Series, I started again.

As I typed away and chugged at my Red Bull, I began thinking back to all of the fantasy and science fiction that had influenced me over the years. Tolken's Lord of the Rings demonstrated that even the shortest and hairiest amongst us may have the opportunity to destroy valuable jewelry. The aforementioned Wheel of Time series opened my eyes to what the term 'epic storytelling' truly meant. Lewis' numerous forays into Narnia allowed me to understand that even a child could wield a sword with enough prompting and that Jesus might have been a lion.

Years of Dungeons and Dragons taught me that not knowing what was around the corner was the most enjoyable part of any journey. With Talisman, Risk and Axis & Allies, I began to understand that while individual conflicts were important, the war must be given as much attention as the battles.

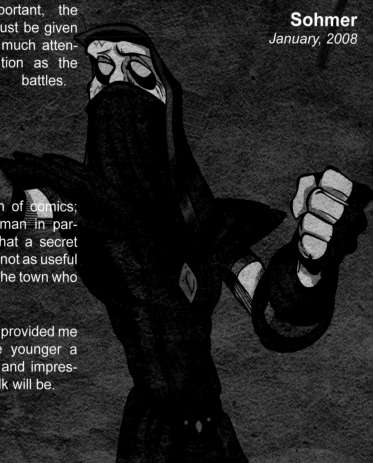

Through my adoration of comics; Spider-Man, X-men and Batman in particular, it became apparent that a secret identity was neat on paper, it's not as useful as a device when you tell half the town who you are under the mask.

And World of Warcraft provided me with the knowledge that the younger a player is, the more profound and impressive his cursing and smack talk will be.

With all that and with a combined 70 years of dorkness between Lar and myself, **Looking For Group** was born.

As that first page of Cale and Richard's adventure lay before us, we came to the immediate decision that we could not give this to anyone, that this series could not be allowed to be used as a graphic infomercial. **LFG** must be nurtured and directed, with us at the helm.

Four issues later and the results are in your hands.

We invite you now to turn the page, leave reality, religion and a sense of right and wrong behind and delve into the first volume of **Looking For Group.**

Oh, and to answer your forthcoming question; many animals *were* harmed in the making of this book.

Especially the cute ones.

Sohmer
January, 2008

LOOKING FOR GROUP

BY RYAN SOHMER & LAR DESOUZA

PICK UP THE PACE, GID. I WANT A SKY OVERHEAD TONIGHT.

WHY DOES HE CALL YOU THAT?

IS HE EVIL TOO?

THAT'S A LOADED QUESTION, PINKY.

KRUNCH PRACTICALLY RAISED ME AND USED TO INTRODUCE ME AS HIS 'GREEN KID'.

OVER THE YEARS IT GOT SHORTENED.

WE ALL DO AS WE MUST TO MAKE OUR WAY IN THIS WORLD AND UNFORTUNATELY SOMETIMES WE HAVE TO DO THING OTHERS MAY QUALIFY AS 'EVIL'.

EITHER GET USED TO THAT IDEA OR YOU'RE NOT GOING TO LAST LONG.

THERE'S A CLEARING UP AHEAD. LET'S KEEP MOVING.

INTRUDERS!

YOU MAY NOT PASS.

FWOOM

YOU MAY PASS.

AND I APOLOGIZE FOR MY EARLIER RUDENESS.

THAT WAS UNQUESTIONABLY EVIL, RIGHT?

ALSO AMUSING

LOOKING FOR GROUP

BY RYAN SOHMER & LAR DESOUZA

COME, PINKY.

LET US LEAVE THIS TOMB AND FACE THE FUTURE YOU'VE CREATED.

ALL IS IN MOTION?

THE PLAYERS ARE SET, THE DIE HAS BEEN CAST.

THUS IT WAS WRITTEN, THUS IT SHALL BE.

INNOCENCE IS THE COST OF JUSTICE.

REMEMBER A FEW MOMENTS AGO WHEN YOU MURDERED A LITTLE BOY?

THAT WAS RATHER ENTERTAINING.

WARLOCK—

NOT THE INNOCENCE OF SOME NON EXISTENT CHILD, BUT OF CALE'ANON, VATAY.

CALE'ANON, KING.

LOOKING FOR GROUP

BY RYAN SOHMER & LAR DESOUZA

FEAR THE LORD OF DARKNESS!

THE PRINCE—

WHY AM I HERE?

WISH I COULD TELL YOU, BUT THE FEAR IS OVERWHELMING ME AT THE MOMENT, MY PRINCE.

TAKE ALL THE TIME YOU NEED.

I UNDERSTAND.

DID MY SUCCESSFUL ATTACK WIN THE DECISIVE VICTORY IN THE BATTLE?

LUCKY FOR YOU, CALE AND PELLA WERE STILL IN EAR SHOT DURING YOUR VERY SUCCESSFUL ATTACK

AND HEARD THE CRACKING OF YOUR BONES.

AFTERWARDS, THE ELF PEELED YOU OFF THE ELEMENTAL'S FOOT AND I HEALED YOU.

MUCH LAUGHTER WAS HAD.

NOW THAT YOU'RE BETTER, I'LL BE JOINING KRUNCH AND THE VILLAGERS, PREPARING FOR THE NEXT ASSAULT.

I—

YOU'RE OF NO USE TO US NOW.

STAY HERE WHERE IT'S SAFE.

I WISH I WERE BIG.

LOOKING FOR GROUP

BY RYAN SOHMER & LAR DESOUZA

PRIESTESS?

WHAT ARE YOU DOING OUT HERE?

PROVING A POINT, THAT EVEN IN MY MINIMIZED STATE, I AM STILL THE LORD OF DARKNESS.

MY AID IS INVALUABLE.

TO ILLUSTRATE SAID POINT, I HAVE LOCATED THE ITEM OF WHICH YOU'VE BEEN SEEKING.

YOU FOUND THE SWORD OF TRUTH?

BEHOLD!

FOOF

THE SWORD OF 77% PROBABILITY!

THE SWORD OF MAYBE, MAYBE NOT!

THE SWORD OF MOSTLY FALSEHOODS.

THE STICK OF LIES.

TAKE YOUR PICK.

A STICK—

I TAKE IT YOU HAVEN'T FIGURED OUT HOW TO DESTROY THE PENDANT AND LIFT THE CURSE?

USING MY AWESOME POWER, IT IS ONLY A MATTER OF TIME.

I AM NOW AWAITING THE RESULTS OF MY MOST RECENT ATTEMPT.

EAT THIS.

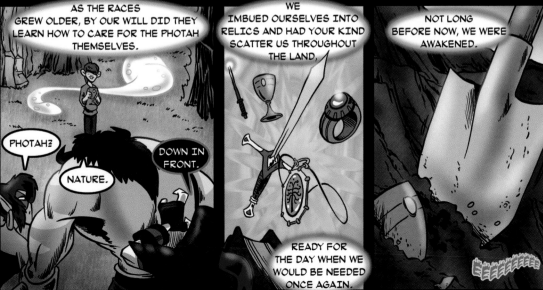

EVIL IS THE NEW LOVE

I HAVE A PANTHER